★ the complete
JUDGE DREDD in

Written by
JOHN WAGNER
ALAN GRANT

Art By

CLIFF ROBINSON STEVE DILLON WILL SIMPSON JIM BAIKIE BRENDAN MCCARTHY

PAUL BEHRER DAVE ELLIOTT JOHN HIGGINS BARRY KITSON

G'day. The first part of this album, in its own small way, surely deserves a place in the Book of Comic Book Records; originally appearing in the 'Galaxy's Greatest Comic', *2000 AD*, it boasts more artists in its first ten instalments than any other story I can remember.

This was not deliberate. The original idea, as conceived by co-writer John Wagner and myself, was for an epic *Judge Dredd* tale to be illustrated by two artists only - Cam Kennedy, whose moody artwork on the Chopper story *Midnight Surfer* was the prime inspiration for this follow-up; and Brendan McCarthy, whose working holiday in Australia produced the sketches and

ideas which led to the creation of the sinister, murderous Judda.

After the initial discussions, however, Cam had to drop out of the project owing to his commitments to DC Comics' *Outcasts* and *Spectre* titles - leaving *2000 AD* editor Richard Burton with a king-sized headache. No artist is capable of turning out seven, eight or nine pages of *Judge Dredd* on a weekly basis - at least not without compromising his talent, not to mention the likelihood of necessary recuperation in a Kook Cube. With deadlines rushing towards him like an out-of-control skysurfer, Richard pulled a solution of Machiavellian simplicity from his Betelgeusian hat. Rather than attempt the impossible, he went for the highly improbable - and managed to create a team of some of Britain's most talented illustrators, none of whom could do the whole job, but each of whom was more than willing to do a part of it.

Cliff Robinson, one of my own favourite *Dredd* artists, kicked off the scene-setting

intro

Part One with some lovely, understated work. Jim Baikie, fresh from his Batman in *Detective Comics* and advised by next-door neighbour Cam Kennedy, did an admirable Part Two in record time. Part Three is credited to Behrer/Spud; not a German potato dish but a partnership between Paul Behrer, Dave Elliott and Will Simpson. The same team also figured in Part Four, this time calling themselves K. Edwards another reference to the mysterious Spud (actually Dave Elliott's nickname, due to his penchant for that vegetable).

Part Five was specially written to allow free rein to Brendan McCarthy's anarchic weirdness, a foretaste of the powerful work he turned in on Parts Seven and Eight (where even Brendan had assistance, from artist Steve Whitaker). Part Six saw Will Simpson stepping forward, helped out by Paul Behrer (who did the spread) and Dave Elliott's inks; later in the story, Will really comes into his own. Finally, with Parts Nine and Ten, long-

time *2000 AD* contributor Steve Dillon showed just why his work is so popular with his fans.

All things considered, it's perhaps surprising that *Judge Dredd in Oz* was ever published at all. But what's even more surprising - almost a minor miracle - is that despite the number of artists, each with his own highly individual style, the story looks and reads so well.

By the time Part 11 was reached, the rota of artists had settled down from its somewhat frenetic beginnings. Through judicious use of two of the best current *Dredd* artists - Barry Kitson and John Higgins, who drew Parts 13 and 20 respectively - the new regular team of Will Simpson and Brendan McCarthy were able to take care of all the other art chores. Brendan in particular had the space to open out and develop his characters, the original sketch for which he'd sent us a couple of years earlier with a suggestion that the characters might form a

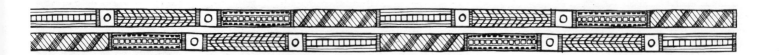

to be rediscovered when we started work on Oz. So much time had elapsed that, when told we were finally going to use the Judda, Brendan had completely forgotten what they looked like. The wait was well worthwhile, though, resulting in some of Brendan's grimmest, most striking illustrations to date.

As co-writer I'm biased, I know, and I must have read this part a dozen times already - but I still laugh out loud when I read the pages featuring Cooky, the manic, ship's galley droid. A robotic hybrid of Sawney Bean and Captain Birdseye, Cooky is the kind of character John and I delight in writing. His love of all things culinary, filtered through his lunatic logic circuits, produces a nightmare from which our hero, Chopper, almost doesn't wake up. But to be appreciated fully, Cooky's speech balloons should be read out loud in your best Long John Silver voice.

gang of rogue Judges living in the Cursed Earth radiation desert. John and I often encourage artists to provide ideas for stories they'd like to illustrate; however, we didn't have an immediate opening for the Judda and the sketch languished in our References File,

Reading our scripts aloud is a device John and I often use when working together, adopting different voices and accents for each character. I don't know if it improves our material any, but it certainly makes working a lot more fun. I have to admit to a fair amount of trouble with the Australian accent - evidently Scotsmen find it hard to master - but for the sake of accuracy we did use an Australian/English dictionary.

At this point, a word for that generally unsung hero of every comic book: the lettering artist. The writers may produce the script - the artist may provide the visual interpretation - but it's the letterer whose skill is crucial in marrying the two into a story. There are approximately 520 word panels and speech balloons in this second part - plus sundry CHUUNGs, BLAMs and KERCHUNKs - every one of which was hand-lettered, positioned and stuck down by that master of the template, Thomas 'Fasthand' Frame. The clarity and thoughtful consistency of Tom's lettering has graced the *Judge Dredd* strip in *2000 AD* almost since its inception ten years ago, and I've no doubt he'll be doing it for the next ten - if only because letterers can never afford to retire. As well as being overlooked and overworked, they're well underpaid.

Any readers fired with a sudden sympathy for a letterer's lot should send their Galactic Groats direct to Tom; tell him you read it here!

Parts 21 to 26 of the *Judge Dredd in Oz* story represents the final material that co-writer and *Judge Dredd* creator John Wagner and myself produced together for a British comic. This brought to an end a writing partnership which had begun some eight years earlier, on the *Dredd* story in *2000 AD* Prog 177. Coincidentally, that episode, too, was part of an epic (*Judge Child*) and was drawn by my all-time favourite *Dredd* artist, Mike McMahon. Mike had no part to play in the *Oz* series, but the influence of his trendsetting style is unmistakeable in its pages. It says much for artists John Higgins, Barry Kitson and Jim Baikie that, while remaining basically true to the McMahon archetype, each produces his own highly personal depiction.

Over the years, the portrayal by John and myself of Dredd had become grimmer and more absurdly totalitarian than John's original version; the Mega-City itself

was now a claustrophobic nightmare where the down-trodden citizens lived on a knife-edge between despair and (usually violent) insanity. As we worked on the *Oz* series, it became clear that our mutual vision of Dredd and his world was starting to diverge. In particular, John wanted to bring a stronger feeling of realism into the story and to show that Dredd still had a human side; I favoured taking the strip even further into a grotesque parody.

The matter was more or less ignored until it erupted into prominence with the climactic pages in Part 26. Until the day we wrote it, we didn't know how *Oz* was going to end. We'd discussed in depth the various possibilities - Chopper winning SuperSurf and escaping; Chopper winning and giving himself up to Dredd; Chopper winning and being granted judicial pardon. The solution - which I won't give away now - was very much a last-minute inspiration (thanks to my wife, Sue), but in the closing scenes, with Dredd threatening to kill the renegade skysurfer, John pointed out just how much time our diverging views were costing us.

John had always liked Chopper as a character and reader popularity backed him up. The unemployed nobody, who was one of the very few to put one over on the world's greatest lawman, went down well with *2000 AD's* audience. My own feeling was that Dredd should kill him. By the time you finish this book, you'll know who won out.

The three parts of *Hit Man*, which neatly round off the *Oz* saga, were written by John on his own and reflect his changing ideas about Dredd's development - ideas which were calculated to usher in the most dramatic upheaval since the character's inception 11 years ago. For further details, read the folllowing progs.

OK then sports: park your bum on the old cane chair, crack open a tube of the amber nectar, and settle down for a ripper read…
Alan Grant, 1988

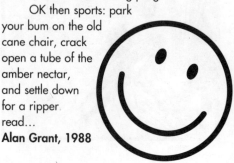

The Complete Judge Dredd in Oz
ISBN 1 85286 436 2
Published by Titan Books Ltd,
19 Valentine Place, London SE1 8QH.

First published in *2000 AD* Progs 545-570.
Compiled by Titan Books into three volumes March - August 1988. This edition first published March 1994.
Judge Dredd is © 1994 Fleetway Publications.

10 9 8 7 6 5 4 3 2

Cover illustration by Bill Sienkiewicz.
Cover design by Nigel Davies based on a concept by Mark Cox.

Printed in Singapore.

Also available from Titan Books:
ABC Warriors: The Black Hole • The Collected Slaine
The Complete Judge Caligula
The Complete Halo Jones • Nemesis: The Beginning

Coming soon:
The Complete Judge Dredd Cursed Earth • The Complete Judge Dredd Apocalypse War

If you have any difficulty finding any of our publications, please write to Titan Books Mail Order,
19 Valentine Place, London SE1 8QH, enclosing a stamped S.A.E. for a reply.

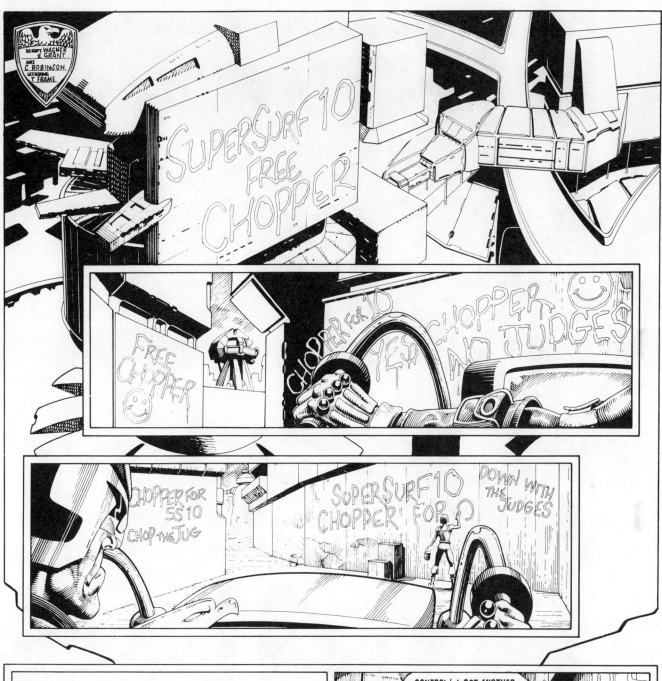
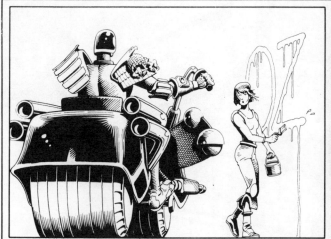

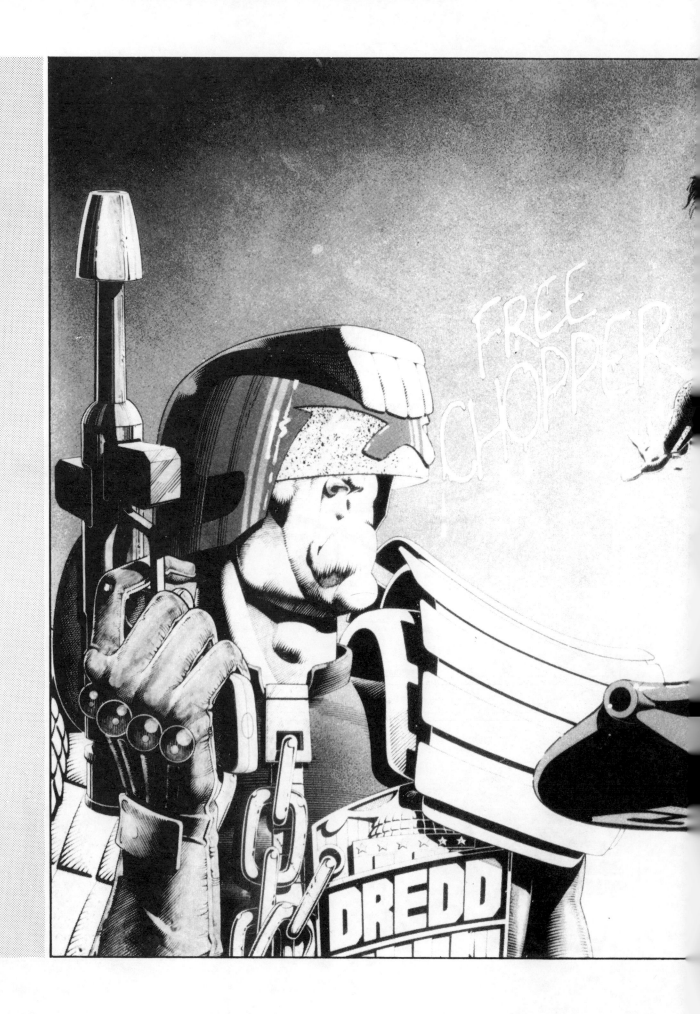

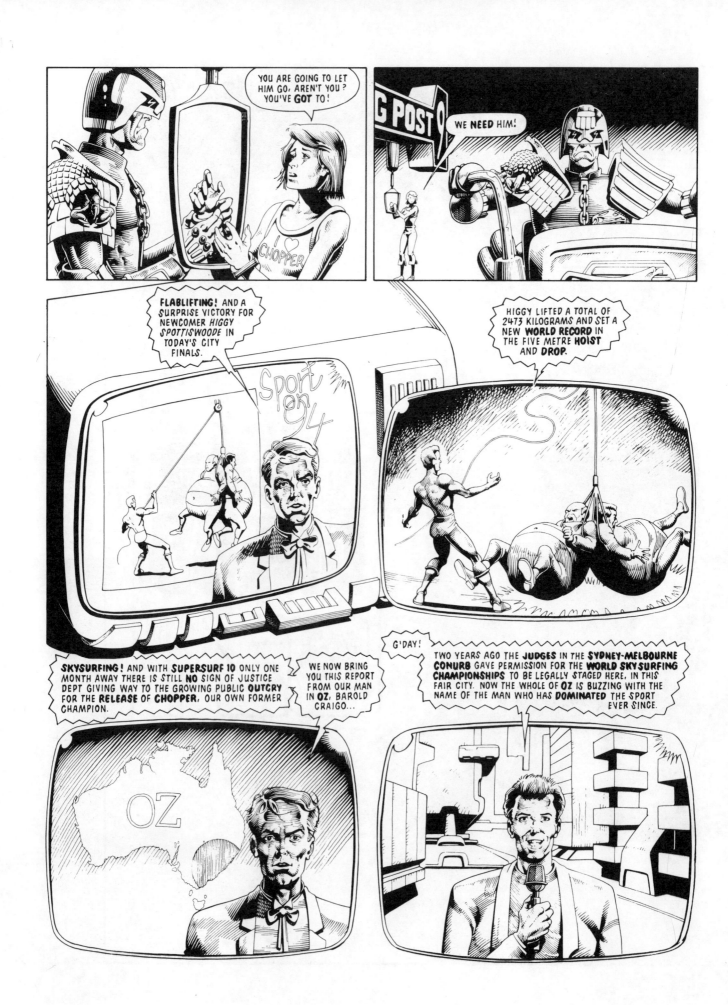

AND IN HIS DREAMS HE RELIVES HIS MOMENT OF GLORY. THE DAY HE DID WHAT NO OTHER SURFER HAD EVER DONE — *SHOT* THE *FOX BACKWARDS...*

...AND THE WHOLE CITY KNEW HIS NAME!

CHOPPER! CHOPPER!

AND HE DREAMS OF FREEDOM. OF BREAKING LOOSE, OF TAKING HIS BOARD AND RIDING IT UP — UP — *UP* INTO THE SKY.

ON AND ON, NEVER STOPPING, DEEP INTO THE COSMOS WHERE NO ONE CAN EVER FIND HIM, NO JUDGE CAN EVER AGAIN CATCH THE *MIDNIGHT SURFER.*

MARLON SHAKESPEARE —

ON YOUR FEET. COME WITH ME.

WHAT'S THIS ABOUT, DREDD — TAKING ME FOR A BEATING?

STILL THE REBEL, HUH? LET'S SEE HOW LIPPY YOU ARE WHEN YOU'VE GOT ANOTHER 15 YEARS UNDER YOUR BELT.

PRISONER MARLON SHAKESPEARE FOR TRANSFER TO ISO-BLOCK 83.

EXAMINE YOUR POSSESSIONS. SIGN HERE, HERE AND HERE.

MY BOARD...

I SAID EXAMINE IT, CREEP — NOT MAKE LOVE TO IT. **SIGN.**

TRANSFER? HOW COME?

DIDN'T YOU HEAR? NO, DON'T SUPPOSE YOU WOULD'VE...

YOU'RE A **STAR** AGAIN, SHAKESPEARE. **SUPERSURF 10** COMING UP IN **OZ** — THERE'S A BIG CAMPAIGN TO HAVE YOU RELEASED TO TAKE PART. WE'RE MOVING YOU TILL THINGS COOL DOWN A BIT.

EXIT

SUPERSURF 10... THREE YEARS. HAS IT BEEN THAT LONG?

THERE HE IS!

CHOPPER!

CHOPPER

CHOPPER

THEY'RE SURGING, DROKK IT! HOLD THEM BACK!

FREE CHOPPER

CHOPPER FOR OZ

CHOPPER FOR OZ!

HE'S USING THE CONVOY! HOLD YOUR FIRE!

JUST A BURN. THEY HAVEN'T GOT ME YET!

ZZAA-AKK!

THEN HE IS FREE AND SPEEDING AWAY —

USING THE COVER OF THE RAVAGED LANDSCAPE, VANISHING INTO THE BLACKNESS OF THE CURSED EARTH NIGHT.

PROG 547
7 NOV 87

$1.70 Malaysia
75c Australia
85c New Zealand
(inc. G.S.T.)
88g Mercury
210g Venus
66g Mars
110g Saturn
2g Pluto
429g Neptune

28P
EARTH
MONEY

2000 AD

FEATURING JUDGE DREDD

IN ORBIT
EVERY
MONDAY

CHOPPER

OUT!

CLIFF ROBINSON '87

SO EXHAUSTED IS HE AFTER HIS ORDEAL THAT HE FALLS TO THE SAND AND SLEEPS, THE SOFT WHISPER OF THE SURF LULLING HIM...

SO EXHAUSTED THAT HE DOES NOT STIR WHEN THE MIDNIGHT BEACH ERUPTS...

...AND THE SOFT, LEATHERY BODIES SCRAMBLE ACROSS HIM IN THEIR RUSH TO THE SEA —

— INTO THE ARMS OF THEIR WAITING ASSASSINS.

JUDGE DREDD

SCRIPT WAGNER/GRANT
ART SIMPSON/REX
LETTERING T. FRAME

OZ PART 6

THE SURVIVOR

HE SLEEPS ON, UNAWARE OF THE PAGEANT OF LIFE AND DEATH BEING PLAYED OUT AROUND HIM NEW LIVES, NEW HOPES – ALL TOO OFTEN CRUELLY SNUFFED OUT BEFORE THEY CAN BEGIN TO FULFIL THEIR POTENTIAL.

YET NOT ALL ARE EXTINGUISHED. SOME GET THROUGH. THE STRONG – THE QUICK – THE LUCKY...

NEXT PROG: ENTER THE JUDDA!

LIES, HALF-TRUTHS AND INCINERATIONS...

$1.80 Malaysia
85c Australia
$1.00 New Zealand (Inc. G.S.T.)
88g Mercury
210g Venus
66g Mars
110g Saturn
2g Pluto
429g Neptune

28p EARTH MONEY

2000AD
FEATURING JUDGE DREDD

PROG 551
5 DEC 87

IN ORBIT EVERY MONDAY

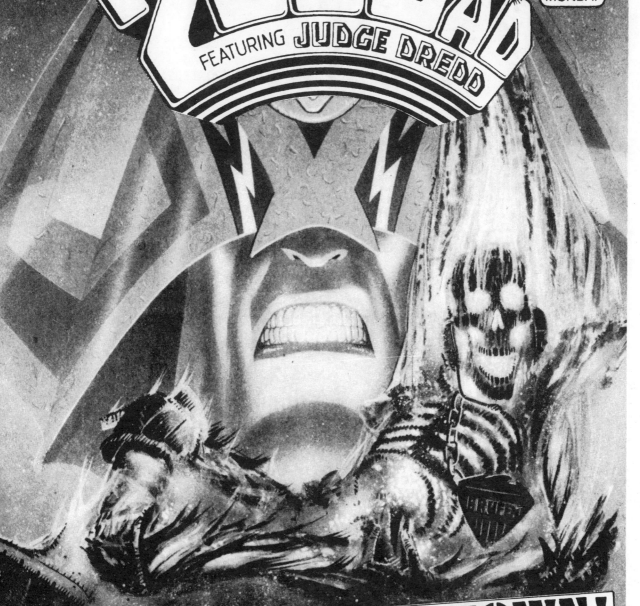

THE JUDDA ARE IN TOWN!

THIS IS BRUFEN. SCRUB THOSE INTRUDERS – GET A MEAT WAGON DOWN HERE.

WILCO.

WHILE I'M ON, YOU GOT THE WHEREABOUTS OF JUDGES MACNAMEE, DREDD AND DEFOE?

SURE... MACNAMEE'S DOWN AT MEG-COM RUNNING A RANDOM CHECK... DREDD'S BUSTIN' HEADS, SIXTH AND SICILY...

DEFOE'S CURRENTLY ON THE BOWL, SECTOR HOUSE 109.

WHY ARE YOU ASKING, BRUFEN?

BRUFEN?

THREE YET TO DIE.

SIMEON – DEFOE.

ZALMAN – MACNAMEE.

DREDD IS MINE.

JUDDA GO WITH US!

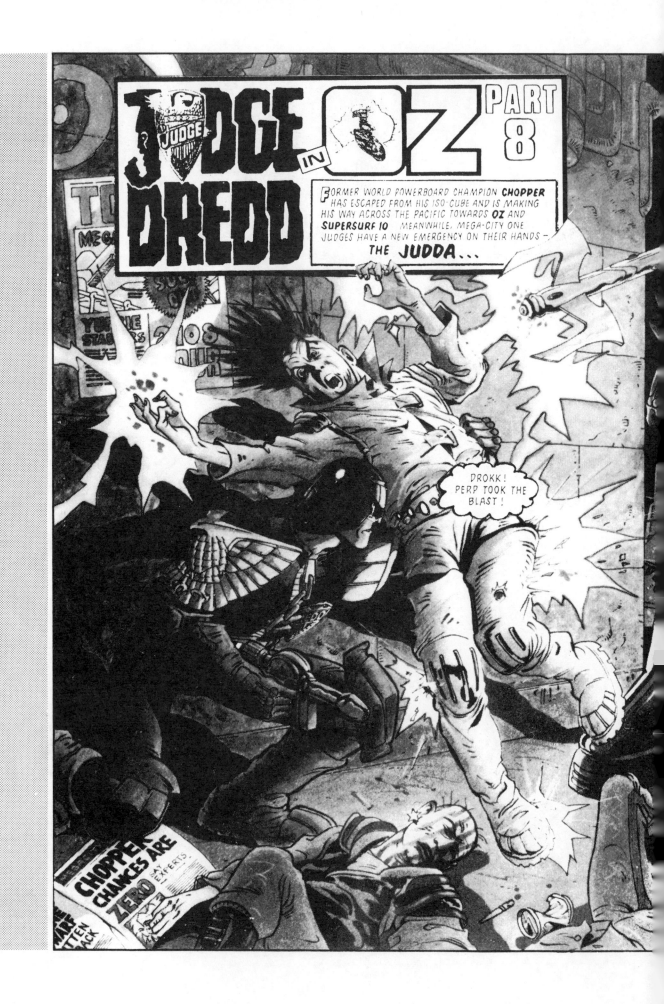

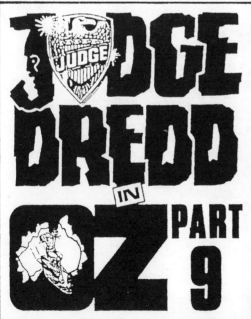

FOR THE FIRST TIME IN HIS LIFE HE FEELS REALLY **FREE**.

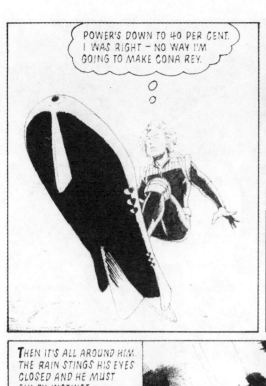

POWER'S DOWN TO 40 PER CENT. I WAS RIGHT — NO WAY I'M GOING TO MAKE CONA REY.

STORM COMING UP TOO. GONNA BE FUN...

THEN IT'S ALL AROUND HIM. THE RAIN STINGS HIS EYES CLOSED AND HE MUST FLY BY INSTINCT —

— FIGHTING AGAINST THE WIND THAT THREATENS EVERY MOMENT TO RIP HIM FROM HIS SLENDER BOARD.

G'DAY! THIS IS **BAROLD GRAIGO** IN THE **SYDNEY/MELBOURNE** CONURB IN THE HEART OF **OZ** WHERE THE CREAM OF THE WORLD'S SKYSURFERS HAVE BEGUN TO ARRIVE FOR NEXT MONTH'S **SUPERSURF 10.**

ALREADY THE AIR IS THICK WITH BOARDERS PUTTING IN SOME EARLY PRACTICE IN THIS SECTION OF THE CITY SPECIALLY SET ASIDE BY THE OZ AUTHORITES.

JUG MCKENZIE, WORLD SKYSURF CHAMPION FOR THE PAST TWO YEARS — WHAT IS YOUR REACTION TO THE NEWS THAT CHOPPER IS ON HIS WAY TO WREST BACK THE TITLE YOU HAVE HELD SINCE HIS IMPRISONMENT?

HANG ON A MINUTE, BAZ — I'M DOING A **COMMERCIAL** HERE...

OKAY, JUG, SUCK THAT TUBE LIKE YOU REALLY MEANT IT! LOOK HAPPY NOW!

CUE **VOICE** OVER —

GLUG GLUG GLUG

"THUNDER CHUNDER XXXX — JUG MCKENZIE, THE WIZARD OF OZ, WOULDN'T GIVE A —

BRUUUPPP!

—FOR ANYTHING ELSE!

HE LOSES TRACK OF HOW LONG HE'S BEEN RIDING THE STORM.

THE HOWLING WIND AND RAIN, THE WILD EXHILARATION, EVERY MOMENT BALANCED ON A KNIFE EDGE – THERE IS NO ROOM FOR ANY OTHER THOUGHT BUT THE BATTLE...

ONE MISTAKE AND HE IS SWEPT FROM THE BOARD...

...DANGLING BY HIS BILLYCORD, TOSSED LIKE A LEAF –

NOT... GONNA BEAT ME... THAT EASY.!.

HELL! MIGHT AS WELL NOT'VE BOTHERED! BOARD'S RUNNIN' ON RED – I'M OUTA JUICE!

WELL, NEVER FIGURED I'D MAKE IT. GOTTA BE RIGHT ONCE IN MY LIFE...

THERE IS NOWHERE TO GO BUT DOWN.

FOR THE LAST TIME HE STRUGGLES TO HIS FEET, TAKING CONTROL OF THE PLUNGING BOARD, DIVING – DOWN, DOWN, HEADLONG TOWARDS THE RAGING OCEAN.

AND IT SEEMS, AS HIS DEATH RUSHES UP TO GREET HIM, THAT HE HEARS VOICES RISING ABOVE THE SCREAM OF THE WIND –

CHOPPER!
CHOPPER!
CHOPPER
CHOPPER!
CHOPPER!
CHOPPER!
CHOPPER!
CHOPPER!
CHOPPER!
CHOPPER!
CHOPPER!
CHOPPER!
CHOPPER!
CHOPPER!
CHOPPER!
CHOPPER!
CHOPPE
CHOPPER!

NEXT PROG: **REQUIEM FOR A SURFER!**

CHOPWATCH

TONIGHT THE CITY WEEPS...

IT IS NOW A FULL WEEK SINCE MEGA-CITY SURF KING CHOPPER WAS LAST SEEN HEADING OUT INTO A PACIFIC STORM. SINCE THEN, DESPITE AN INTENSIVE SEARCH, THERE HAS BEEN NO SIGN.

CHOPPER'S VALIANT ATTEMPT TO REACH OZ AND SUPERSURF 10 IS OVER. HE MUST NOW BE PRESUMED DEAD.

"WIPE-OUT" JONES, OUR RESIDENT EXPERT, YOU'RE OFF TO OZ YOURSELF, NOW?

YEAH, BUT WITH A HEAVY, LIKE, HEART, MAN.

CHOP WAS THE TOP – THE CREAM A THE CLOUDS. I AIN'T FIT TO SURF IN HIS SLIP, BUT I GUESS SOMEBODY'S GOTTA UPHOLD THE HONOUR OF THE BIG MEG...

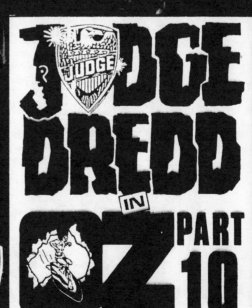

CHOPPER BEAT THE CUBES — HE BEAT THE WALL — HE BEAT THE CURSED EARTH... BUT IN THE END THE ODDS WERE JUST STACKED TOO HIGH AGAINST HIM. YES, TONIGHT THE CITY WEEPS...

TONIGHT... A HERO IS DEAD.

CRUCIN...

JUDGE

JUDGE DREDD IN OZ PART 10

SCRIPT WAGNER & GRANT
ART STEVE DILLON
LETTERING T FRAME

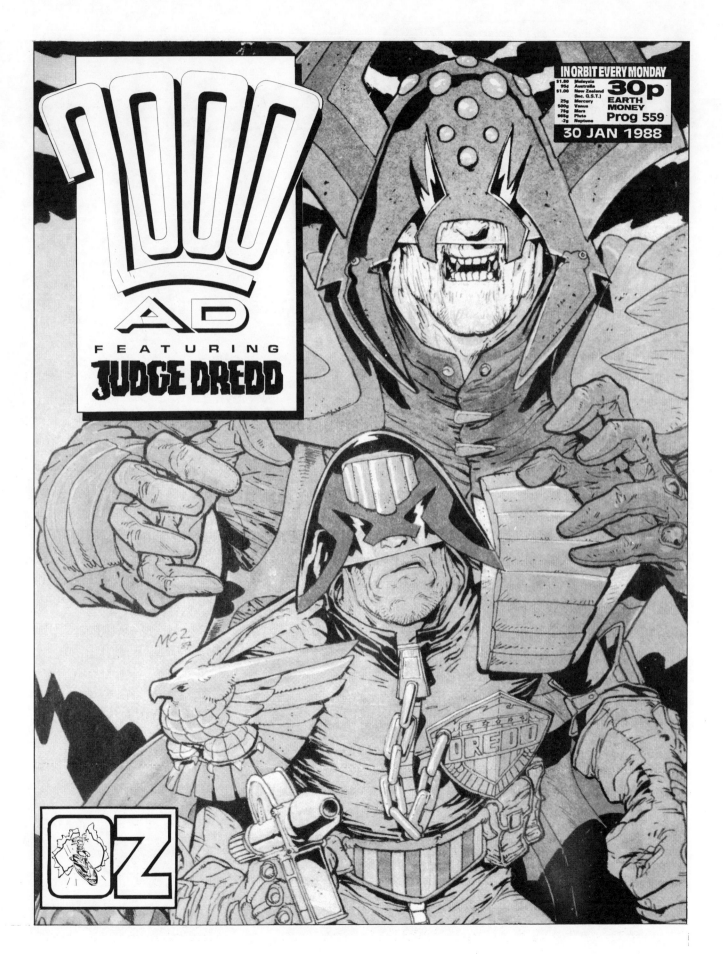

HE IS BARELY 300 METRES UP,
DIVING TOWARDS HIS DEATH,
WHEN HE SEES IT – A FAINT
GLOW THROUGH THE SHEETING
RAIN...

MOLEY–!
IT CAN'T BE!

A SHIP!

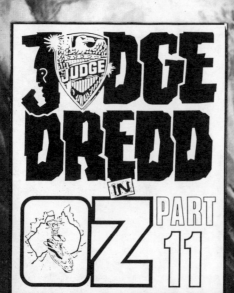

SHIPWRECKED

NEXT PROG: **CHOPPER CHOPPED?**

MARLON SHAKESPEARE, ALIAS **CHOPPER**, HAS ESCAPED FROM A MEGA-CITY ISO-CUBE AND IS CROSSING THE PACIFIC TOWARDS *OZ* AND **SUPERSURF 10**.

BUT NOW, ABOARD A SHIP IN MID-OCEAN...

ARR, JIM LAD! I DID FER THE CREW AN' I'LL DO FER YOU, TOO!

HOLD STILL, DAMN YE!

CHONKK!

CHOPPER FOR OZ!

JUDGE DREDD IN OZ PART 12

SCRIPT WAGNER/GRANT
ART WILL SIMPSON
LETTERING TOM FRAME

SHRAAK!

OO-AAH!

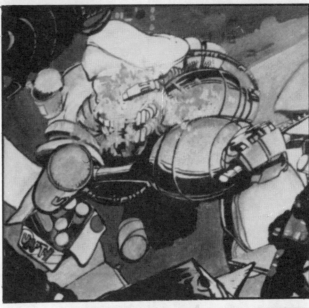

YOU CRAZY ROBOT! THERE'S NO NEED FOR THIS! JUST OPEN THAT DOOR AND LET ME GO!

WHY SHOULD I, MATEY? YE HATES ME, DON'T YE?

NO! I NEVER MET YOU TILL HALF AN HOUR AGO!

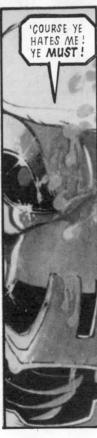

'COURSE YE HATES ME! YE MUST!

LOOK AT THE MESS YE'VE MADE O' ME KITCHEN!

HERO'S WELCOME!

SCRIPT WAGNER & GRANT
ART BARRY KITSON
LETTERING FRAME

"HIS BOARD IS PATCHED — HIS FACE IS GAUNT — HE LOOKS LIKE HE'S BEEN THROUGH HELL — AND WELL HE MIGHT!

"ALL THE WAY FROM MEGA-CITY ONE ON A FLIMSY POWERBOARD! NOBODY BELIEVED IT COULD BE DONE! BUT HE'S MADE IT! HE'S HERE!

"CHOPPER FOR OZ!"

NEXT PROG: RE-ENTER THE JUDDA!

"IN THE BEGINNING WAS JUDD.

"JUDD WAS ALL-WISE AND ALL-SEEING. AND RIGHTEOUSNESS SHONE FROM HIM. BUT THE RULERS OF HIS CITY WERE ONE WITH THE DEVIL. AND WHEN JUDD CAME FORWARD TO TAKE HIS RIGHTFUL PLACE THEY CONSPIRED AGAINST HIM AND CAST HIM OUT INTO THE WILDERNESS.

"THERE IN THAT BARREN PLACE JUDD LABOURED, AND CREATED HE THE JUDDA PURE IN MIND AND RIGHTEOU IN HEART. YEA, EVEN LIKE UNTO JUDD HIMSELF...

THE LOST TRIBE

JUDGE DREDD IN OZ — PART 15

"AND WHEN JUDD SAW THAT THEY WERE READY, HE SENT THEM FORTH TO SMITE THE DEVIL IN HIS LAIR —"

SCRIPT WAGNER & GRANT
ART B. McCARTHY
LETTERING T. FRAME

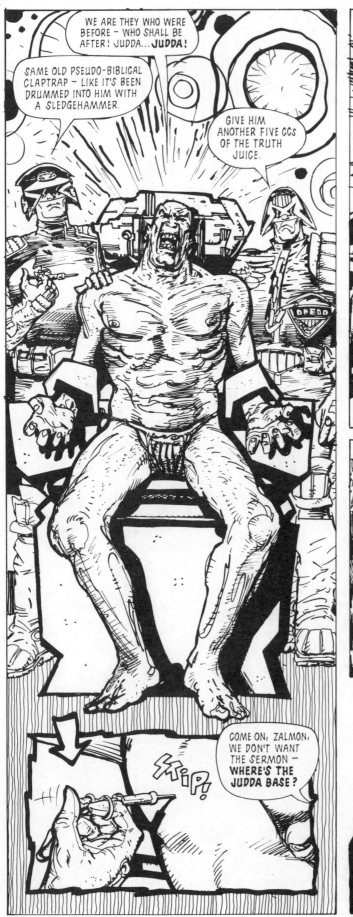

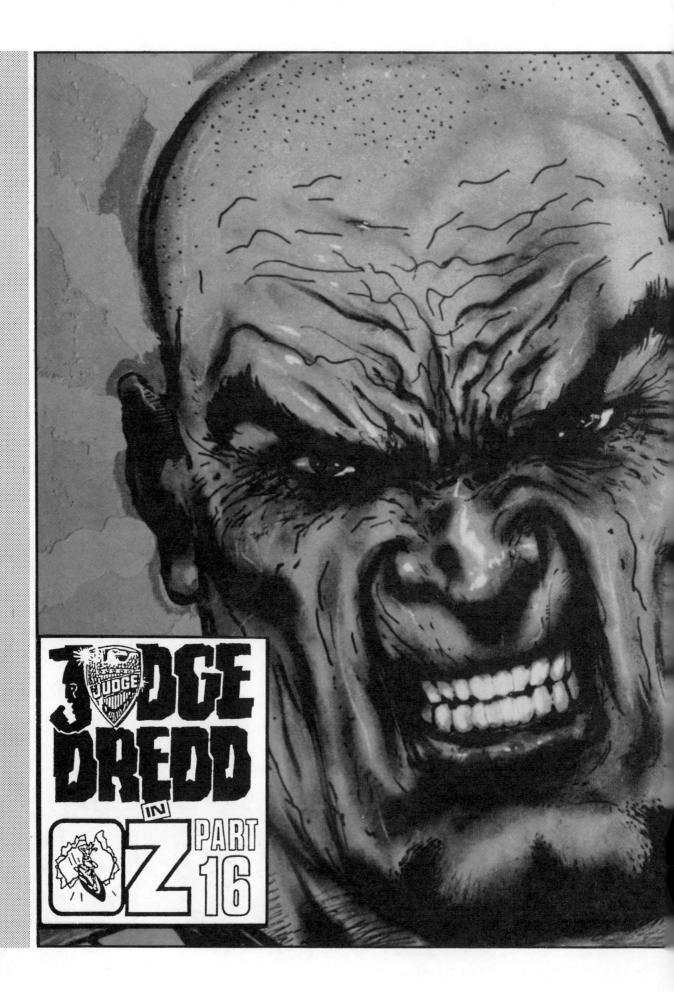

HALLS OF JUDDA

SOMEWHERE IN OZ, WHERE DREDD HAS USED A CAPTURED TELEPORTER TO LOCATE THE HIDDEN STRONGHOLD OF THE JUDDA – THE LOST TRIBE OF JUDGES...

TUNNEL'S TOO NARROW! I'M TRAPPED!

JUDGE DREDD IN OZ PART 17

THERE IS NO WAY OUT, IMPOSTER! THROW DOWN YOUR WEAPONS AND COME OUT!

SCRIPT WAGNER/GRANT
ART WILL SIMPSON
LETTERING TOM FRAME

KNEEL! KNEEL IN THE PRESENCE OF JUDD!

I DON'T KNEEL FOR ANYONE — ESPECIALLY TRAITORS!

KNEEL!

YOU SHOULD TREAT ME WITH MORE RESPECT, JOE DREDD. AFTER ALL, I AM, IN A WAY, YOUR FATHER.

BULL!

YOU SCOFF, BUT REMEMBER — THESE ARE THE HANDS THAT CREATED YOU.

ANY MONKEY CAN SHAKE A TEST TUBE, JUDD. I'M GLAD TO SAY THERE'S NONE OF YOU IN ME.

SACRILEGE! FOR THAT YOU BURN, IMPOSTER!

STAY YOUR HAND, MY JUDDA!

HOW LIKE FARGO YOU ARE!

WELL, YOU'RE WRONG ABOUT ME — JUST AS HE WAS WRONG. HE SCORNED MY IDEAS, BUT I KNEW I WAS RIGHT. MY WAY WAS THE FUTURE...

BUT LIKE MANY A PROPHET BEFORE, I WAS FORCED TO FLEE — TO HIDE FAR AWAY FROM THE EYES OF MY ENEMIES.

AND HERE, IN THIS BARREN PLACE, I FOUND THE PERFECT SANCTUARY IN WHICH TO WORK — TO PLAN — TO MAKE MY DREAM A REALITY.

IT WAS HARD AT FIRST. BUT I HAD MY FAITHFUL DISCIPLES TO AID ME — REEVER, MOYERS, WITHERO, SIMPSON — AND OTHERS. GOOD MEN — FINE MEN.

IT WAS THEIR GENIUS WHICH DEVELOPED MY TECHNOLOGIES, WHICH FED AND CLOTHED AND SUPPORTED US WHILE I CARRIED ON MY MAJOR WORK — THE CREATION OF A NEW BREED — THE JUDDA!

SIGNALS COMING FROM DIRECTLY OVER THE ROCK!

THAT BAT — IT'S COMING FROM THE BAT!

Ping! Ping!

STREWTH, DREDD, WHAT'VE THEY **DONE** TO YOU?

THEY GOTTA BE IN THE ROCK SOMEWHERE! LET'S SHAKE 'EM UP A BIT AN' SEE WHAT FALLS OUT!

NOW YOU UNDERSTAND WHY YOU MUST DIE, JOE DREDD — WHY ALL MEGA-CITY JUDGES MUST PERISH!

YEAH. LIKE I SAID, YOU'RE A CRACKPOT.

KRUNKK!

WE'RE **UNDER** ATTACK!

N**EXT PROG**: **FALL! THE HALLS OF JUDD!**

THE HALLS OF JUDD!

AHHH!

AND **THIS IS IT!**

LOOKS LIKE I'M GETTING OUT JUST IN TIME... UNFORTUNATELY, SO ARE THIS MANIAC'S HIT SQUADS!

SO LONG, CREEP! WITH A BIT OF LUCK YOUR CRAZED DREAMS COULD STILL COME TO NOTHING!

CHIEF JUDGE~!

HOLD YOUR FIRE! IT'S **ME!**

DREDD! BUT YOU'RE MEANT TO BE —

NEXT PROG: **BLOCKBUSTER!**

AYERS ROCK, DEEP IN THE HEART OF THE OZ RADBACK, WHERE DREDD HAS LED OZ JUDGES TO THE SECRET BASE OF **THE JUDDA** —

STREWTH! IT'LL TAKE A FLAMIN' **NUKE** TO GET THROUGH THAT LOT!

MEANWHILE, ACROSS THE GLOBE IN MEGA-CITY ONE'S GRAND HALL OF JUSTICE —

ALERT! ALERT! WE ARE UNDER **JUDDA** ATTACK!

AAGH!

FZAAK!

THAT **NUKE'S** ON A **TEN SECOND** FUSE! YOU'LL BLOW US ALL TO GRUD!

NOT IF I CAN HELP IT! GET BACK!

SCRIPT WAGNER/GRANT
ART WILL SIMPSON
LETTERING T. FRAME

DETONATE

JUDGE DREDD IN **OZ** PART **19**

DROKK! WHAT —?

TELEPORTER! IT'S ON ITS WAY STRAIGHT INTO THE **HALLS OF JUDD!**

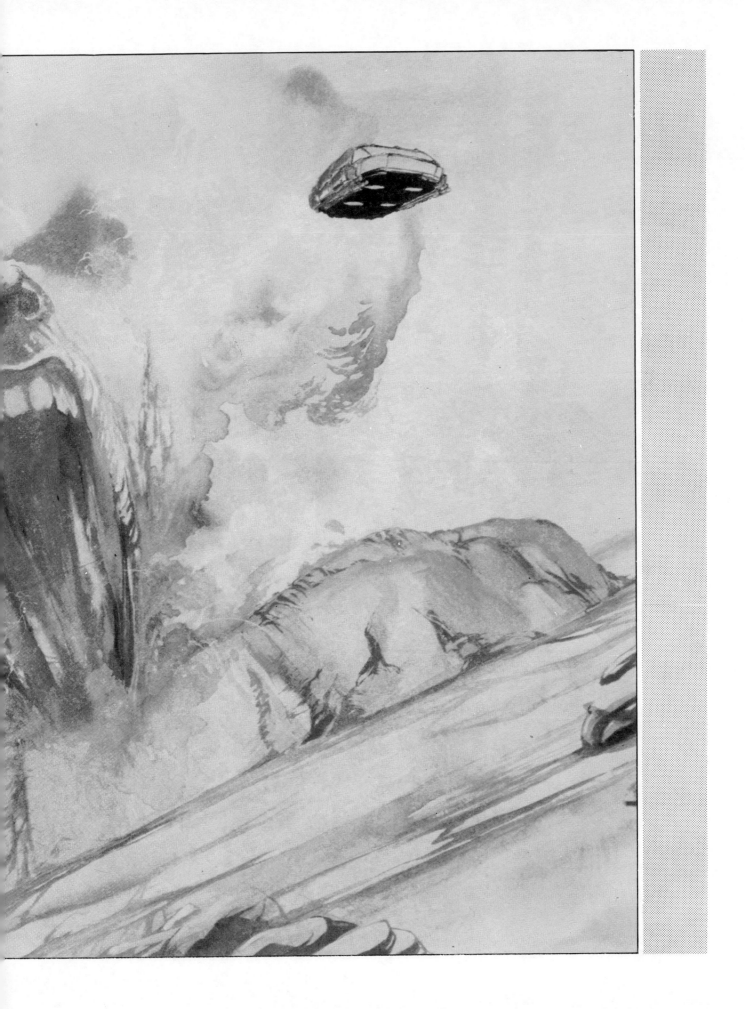

OH, WELL ORDAINED, DREDD!

CRASHH!

THERE REMAINS ONLY THE MOPPING-UP OPERATION –

THE JUDDA, AT LAST REALISING THAT DEFEAT IS INEVITABLE, KNOW NOTHING BUT THE CREED OF JUDD; THEY CHOOSE TO FIGHT TO THE BITTER END –

ONLY A FEW ARE TAKEN ALIVE –

SOME CHOOSE TO TELEPORT OUT, TO RETURN TO THEIR BASE –

— ONLY TO DIE IN THE RADIOACTIVE FURNACE THAT ONCE WAS *JUDD'S ROCK.*

THE HALL OF JUSTICE IS DECLARED ALL CLEAR —

GOOD WORK, DREDD. WITHOUT YOU —

IT DOESN'T BEAR THINKING ABOUT!

EVEN WITH ME IT WAS TOUCH AND GO.

AND ALL BECAUSE OF ONE MAN'S LUST FOR POWER...

CONFIRMATION FROM OZ —

INCREDIBLE... ALL THOSE YEARS HIDDEN INSIDE THAT ROCK... PLANNING — BUILDING — DREAMING OF THE DAY WHEN HE'D OWN THIS CITY.

SUCH DEDICATION — SUCH DRIVE! SUCH SINGLENESS OF PURPOSE! IF ONLY IT COULD HAVE BEEN HARNESSED FOR THE GOOD OF THE CITY...

YES. YOU'VE GOT TO ADMIRE THE MAN...

IN OTHER CIRCUMSTANCES *JUDD* WOULD HAVE MADE A FIRST RATE CHIEF JUDGE.

NEXT PROG:
COUNTDOWN TO SUPERSURF

JUDGE DREDD IN OZ PART 20

OZ. TWO HOURS TO SUPERSURF 10.

THE STREETS ALONG THE ROUTE HAVE BEEN CLEARED, SAVE FOR THE **MED** AND **EMERGENCY** SQUADS. VID CAMS ARE IN PLACE AT EVERY VANTAGE POINT. WINDOWS AND BALCONIES ARE FILLED WITH EAGER SPECTATORS.

THEY'RE SELLING WINDOW SPACE AT A HUNDRED BUCKS A HEAD —

C'MON IN! ICE CREAMS, 'OTTIES, PROGRAMMES, AN' A WIDE RANGE OF MERCHANDISE AVAILABLE FROM THE MISSUS!

TWO HOURS TO GO, AND ALREADY THEY SEARCH THE SKIES IN ANTICIPATION.

A HUNDRED BUCKS — AND FOR WHAT? A FEW BRIEF MOMENTS OF SPECTACLE — OF NERVE-SHATTERING EXCITEMENT. A MEMORY TO CHERISH FOR THE REST OF THEIR LIVES...

WORTH EVERY DOLLAR — AND MORE.

SCRIPT WAGNER/GRANT
ART JOHN HIGGINS
LETTERING T. FRAME

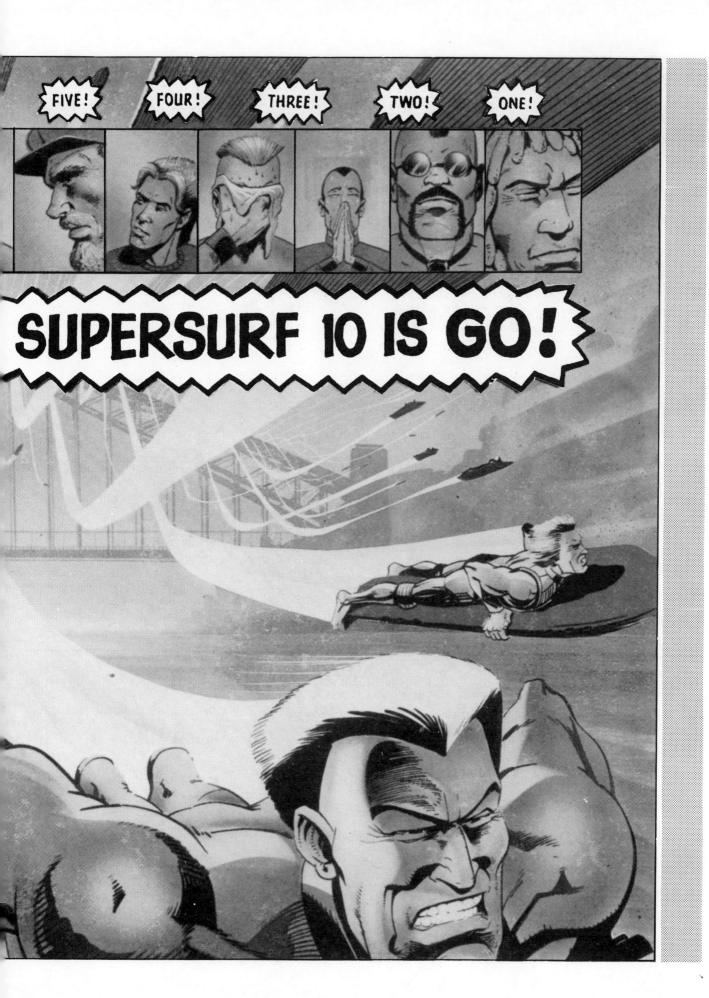

CONTINUED IN
JUDGE DREDD IN OZ BOOK THREE

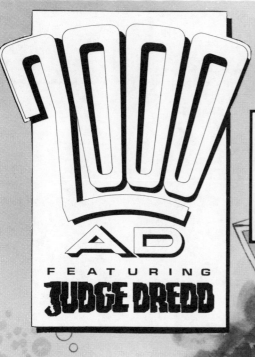

2000 AD
FEATURING
Judge Dredd

IN ORBIT EVERY MONDAY

30p
EARTH
MONEY
Prog 570

16 APR 1988

$1.80 Malaysia
95c Australia
$1.00 New Zealand
(inc. G.S.T.)
25g Mercury
500g Venus
75g Mars
965g Pluto
-2g Neptune

AND THE LOSER IS...

DEATH OR GLORY FOR CHOPPER?

AHEAD THE FIRST DANGER POINT — THE GLEAMING SOLAR SAILS OF THE OZ ROYAL YACHT, DAME EDNA —

JUDGE DREDD IN OZ PART 21

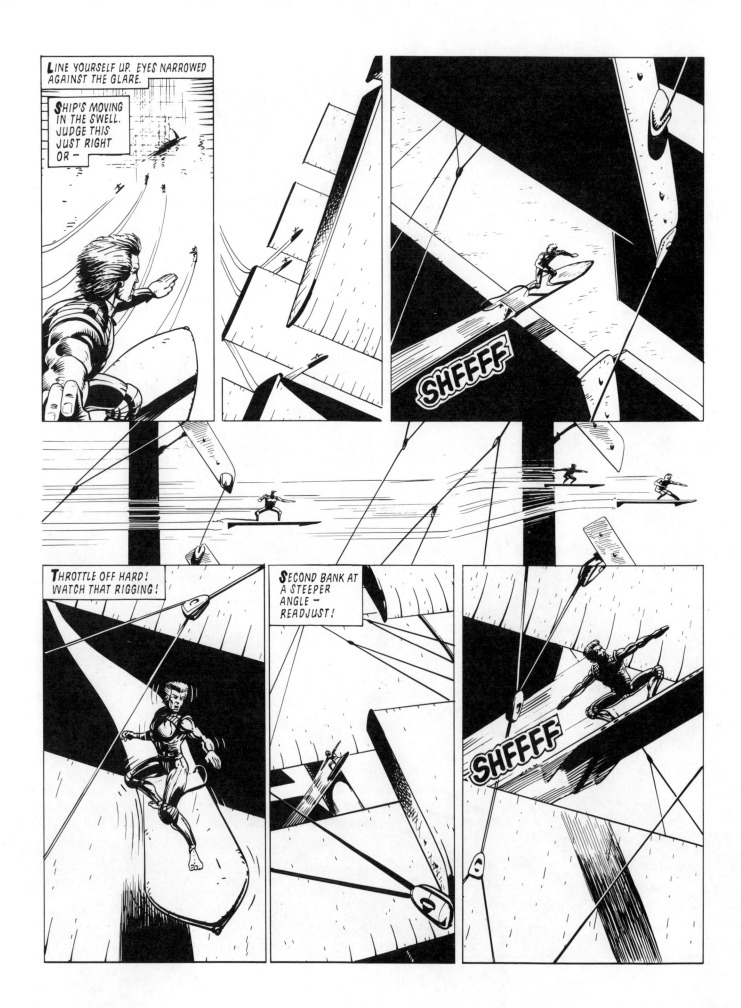

NEXT PROG: **WIPE OUT!**

2000 AD
FEATURING
JUDGE DREDD

IN ORBIT EVERY MONDAY

$1.80 Malaysia
95c Australia
$1.00 New Zealand
(Inc. G.S.T.)
25g Mercury
500g Venus
75g Mars
965g Pluto
-2g Neptune

30p
EARTH
MONEY
Prog 567

26 MAR 1988

THE BIG WET
SUPERSURF 10 DOWN THE TUBES!

JUDGE DREDD

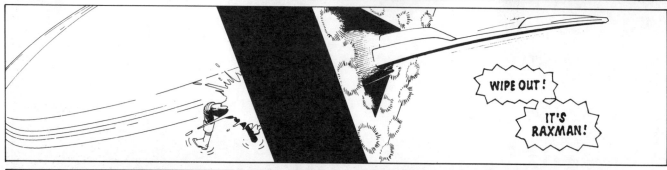

WIPE OUT!

IT'S RAXMAN!

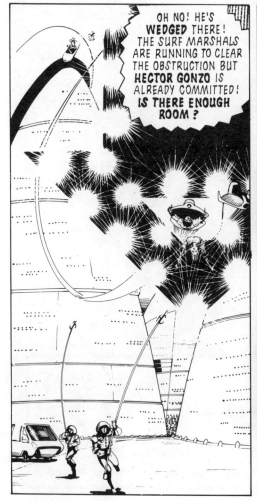

OH NO! HE'S **WEDGED** THERE! THE SURF MARSHALS ARE RUNNING TO CLEAR THE OBSTRUCTION BUT **HECTOR GONZO** IS ALREADY COMMITTED! **IS THERE ENOUGH ROOM?**

NO! SCRATCH HECTOR GONZO!

BUT WE HAVE CLEARWAY! AND THE OTHERS ARE COMING THROUGH!

UHURU – LE PLANQ – JONES – CHEEVER! THEY'RE ALL THROUGH! BUT THEY HAVE DISTANCE TO MAKE UP!

THEY'RE COMING DOWN THE BOULEVARD TURNING INTO THE LONG STRAIGHT OF IFIELD WAY! IT'S **CHOPPER!** STILL GOING STRONG ON HIS BORROWED STRATOS 4! TEN METRES BEHIND IT'S JUG McKENZIE ON HIS BONDI SPECIAL!

TAKE HIM, JUG!

GO IT THE WIZARD!

HALF A WORLD AWAY IN MEGA-CITY ONE TRAFFIC HAS DRIED TO A TRICKLE. THE WHOLE CITY'S STAYING HOME TONIGHT.

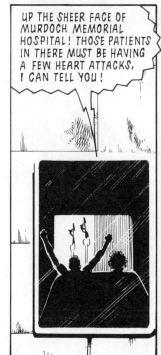

UP THE SHEER FACE OF MURDOCH MEMORIAL HOSPITAL! THOSE PATIENTS IN THERE MUST BE HAVING A FEW HEART ATTACKS, I CAN TELL YOU!

McKENZIE'S GAINING! THREE METRES – TWO –

THIS IS WHERE THE EXTRA POWER OF THE HEAVIER BOARD PAYS ITS DIVIDENDS!

C'MON, CHOPPER!

GO CHOP! DON'T STOP!

AS THEY CLEAR THE CROCKSHOP AND HEAD DOWN TOWARDS THE **FUN PARK** THEY'RE NECK AND NECK! NO! McKENZIE'S JUST AHEAD!

MURDOCH MEMORIAL HOSPITAL

GO, JUG! GO!

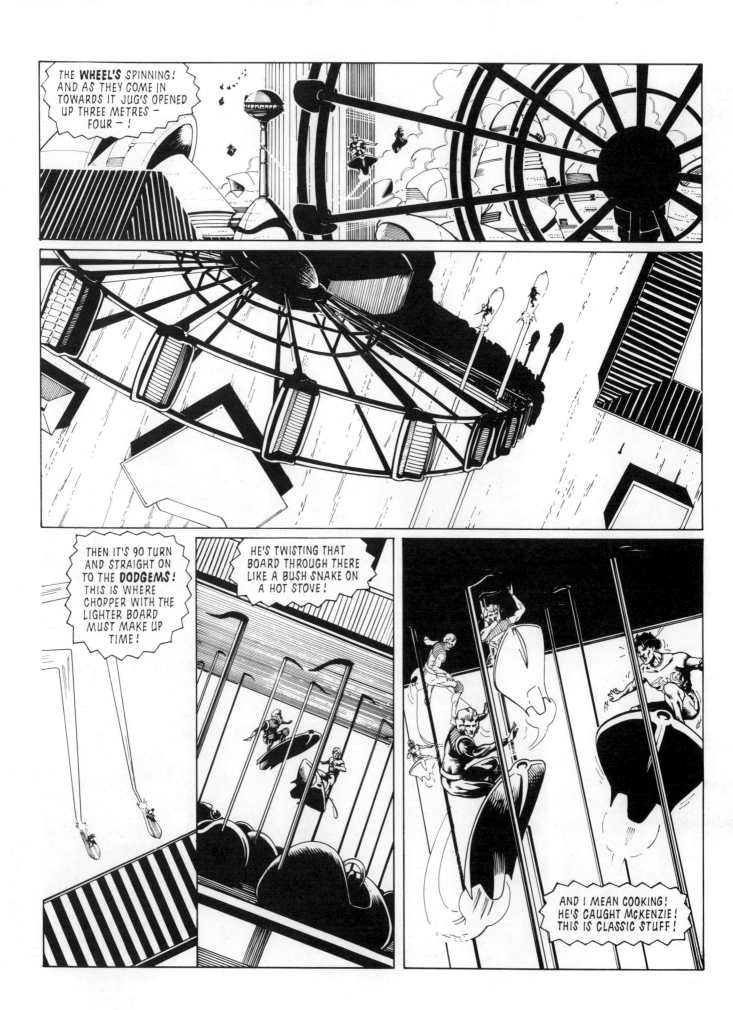

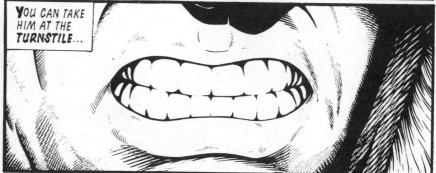

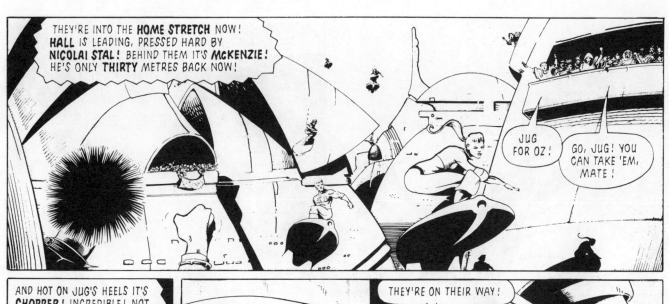

THEY'RE INTO THE **HOME STRETCH** NOW! **HALL** IS LEADING, PRESSED HARD BY **NICOLAI STAL**! BEHIND THEM IT'S **MCKENZIE**! HE'S ONLY **THIRTY** METRES BACK NOW!

JUG FOR OZ!

GO, JUG! YOU CAN TAKE 'EM, MATE!

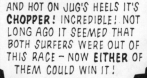

AND HOT ON JUG'S HEELS IT'S **CHOPPER**! INCREDIBLE! NOT LONG AGO IT SEEMED THAT BOTH SURFERS WERE OUT OF THIS RACE – NOW **EITHER** OF THEM COULD WIN IT!

THEY'RE ON THEIR WAY!

SHUT 'EM OFF AND MOVE 'EM OUT!

TORCH IT!

FWOOMPF!

YA FLAMIN' BEAUTY!

SOME FINISH THIS IS GONNA BE!

HITMAN
PART ONE

...MORNING, MEGA-CITY ONE. IT'S MIDNIGHT HERE AND OZ IS STILL JUMPING LIKE A LIZARD ON A HOTPLATE. **SUPERSURF 10** IS OVER BUT THE CELEBRATIONS WILL GO ON FOR MANY A DAY!

ALL THE EXCUSES HAVE BEEN TROTTED OUT...CHOPPER'S LAST-MINUTE CHANGE OF BOARD – FATIGUE – HIS LONG ABSENCE FROM THE SPORT... CERTAINLY NOT THE BEST PREPARATION FOR THE WORLD'S PREMIER SURF EVENT –

SCRIPT WAGNER & GRANT
ART JIM BAIKIE
LETTERING T FRAME

HOW TO TAKE OUT GIRLS

TECHNIQUES OF MURDER

DETERMINATION IN EXTERMINATION AND EXPLANATION

LET THEM EAT LEAD

AND WHAT OF CHOPPER?

MARLON SHAKESPEARE (CHOPPER) (DIED 9TH MAY 2110)

LAST SEEN HEADING OUT INTO THE OZ RADBACK – CAN HE SURVIVE IN THAT HOSTILE ENVIRONMENT? WILL JUDGES MOUNT A HUNT FOR HIM?

BUT OUT HERE NOBODY'S INTERESTED! THE WIZARD HAS CAST HIS SPELL OVER OZ! SO LET'S ALL RAISE A **JUG** TO **JUG MCKENZIE**, THREE TIMES SUPERSURF CHAMPION, PROBABLY THE GREATEST SURFBOARDER WHO HAS EVER LIVED!

THANK YOU, BAROLD. WELL, A "G'DAY" IN OZ BUT A BAD NIGHT FOR JUDGES HERE IN THE MEG AS CRIMES OF VIOLENCE SOARED TO AN ALARMING 73 PER CENT ABOVE THE SEASONAL NORM IN THE HOURS FOLLOWING CHOPPER'S SHOCK DEFEAT.

MELINA CASTRANOVA
ACTRESS
(DIED 4 OCT 2108)

NIKOS BULMER
BALLET DANCER
(DIED 12 DEC 2108)

COURTLAND PHIBES
COUNCILLOR
(DIED 29 JAN 2110)

JUDGE DREDD

SUICIDES REACHED AN ALL-TIME RECORD. JUDGES BELIEVE THERE MAY BE MORE VICTIMS OF SUPERSURF AS YET UNDISCOVERED—

CITIZENS ARE ASKED TO CHECK ON THEIR NEIGHBOURS AND REPORT ANY SUSPICIOUS CIRCUMSTANCES.

LATEST RUMOUR IS THAT THE MEGA-CITY SURFER MAY BE GRANTED UNOFFICIAL ASYLUM. A PROTEST HAS BEEN LODGED WITH OZ AUTHORITIES.

WARNING POSSESSION BY UNAUTHORISED PERSONS IS A SERIOUS OFFENCE

MEANWHILE AN **EXPLOSION** ROCKED HOVERPORT 2 AS JUDGE DREDD ARRIVED HOME FROM OZ. EIGHT DEMONSTRATORS ARE REPORTED DEAD. EYEWITNESSES DESCRIBE THE SCENE AS ONE OF HORRIFIC CARNAGE...

REMOTE CONTROL DETONATOR
INDUSTRIAL USE ONLY

FLIGHT OMC 1435 IS NOW DISEMBARKING AT GATE 17.

PASSENGERS ARE REMINDED TO HAVE ALL VISAS AND TRAVEL DOCUMENTS READY.

THE PROBLEM WAS ALWAYS GOING TO BE GETTING THE BOMB CLOSE ENOUGH!

GATE 17 – THIS WAY! C'MON!

I KNEW I COULD RELY ON THE MAGGOTS. THEY'RE ALWAYS THERE.

C'MON, SHIRL! WE'LL MISS HIM!

I'M TERRIBLY SORRY. I DIDN'T SEE YOU...

YOU SHOULD BE MORE CAREFUL.

uhhhhhh

IT SHOULD HAVE BEEN **CHOPPER**.

I ALREADY HAD HIM ON THE WALL — DATE AND EVERYTHING! I WANTED HIM BAD... DREDD HAD TO GO AND SPOIL IT! HE HAD TO LET HIM GET AWAY! IT WAS ONLY FAIR HE SHOULD TAKE CHOPPER'S PLACE!

HELP ME...

OH MY GOD!

IT WAS ONLY WHEN I GOT HOME I FOUND OUT HE WAS STILL ALIVE.

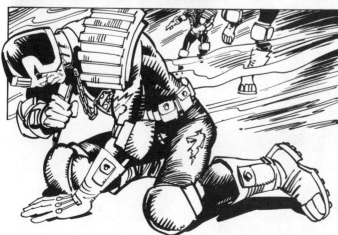

WELCOME HOME.

ONCE I MADE UP MY MIND TO GO FOR DREDD I KNEW IT WAS THE RIGHT DECISION.

SO YOU STATIONED YOURSELF NEAR HIS APARTMENT BLOCK?

JUDGE DREDD

KKRRSHHH!

AH, MEDICAL RECORDS... NOW... WHERE ELSE WOULD YOU HAVE ME?

HMMM?

WH...WHY...?

I HATE TO LOSE YOU, DOC, BUT YOU JUST KNOW TOO MUCH.

I...WOULDN'T HAVE...TOLD

THAT'S WHAT YOU SAY. BUT YOU'RE JUST LIKE ANYONE ELSE. ONCE THE JUDGES COME SNIFFING AROUND —

AND YOU KNOW THEY'RE GOING TO PULL OUT ALL THE STOPS ON THIS ONE.

WE FIGURE IT'S GOT TO BE THE SAME ONE WHO TRIED FOR YOU AT THE HOVER PORT. WE'VE PULLED IN OVER FOUR HUNDRED SUSPECTS SO FAR. SOME GOOD ARRESTS, BUT NEGATIVE ON YOUR MAN.

THE TROUBLE IS THERE ARE SO MANY PEOPLE WITH GOOD REASON TO HATE YOU.

MY FAULT... I SHOULD'VE NAILED HIM.

THE FIRST BULLET PENETRATED YOUR LUNG. YOU WERE IN NO POSITION—

BEFORE THAT...

I CAN USUALLY SMELL TROUBLE. I SHOULD'VE BEEN READY. BUT LAST NIGHT... NOTHING.

TWO BAD MISTAKES...

TWO?

CHOPPER.

WE'VE BEEN THROUGH THIS BEFORE, DREDD. THE OZZER RAMMED YOU.

"I HAD PLENTY TIME TO MAKE THE SHOT. BUT I DIDN'T. EVEN NOW I DON'T KNOW WHETHER I COULD HAVE..."

"I DON'T KNOW WHY... I GUESS I ADMIRED HIM. THE KID HAD CLASS... SEEMED TO ME HE DESERVED BETTER THAN A BULLET IN THE BACK."

AND YET THE LAW — THE MAINTENANCE OF GOOD ORDER — THAT SHOULD HAVE BEEN THE FIRST CONSIDERATION.

WE ALL MAKE MISTAKES, DREDD, THOUGH WE DON'T OFTEN CARE TO ADMIT IT. IF YOU ACTED LIKE A HUMAN BEING FOR ONCE, I'M NOT GOING TO HOLD IT AGAINST YOU.

"IF IT CONTINUES TO WORRY YOU, SEE THE SHRINK. IN THE MEANTIME LET'S CONCENTRATE ON CRACKING THE REAL NUT."

FRANK GILBRET
PRIVATE SHRINK

FRANK GILBRET
PRIVATE SHRINK

"I THINK WE CAN BE FAIRLY CERTAIN WE HAVEN'T HEARD THE LAST OF HIM."

NEXT PROG: **SITTING TARGET !**

2000 AD

FEATURING **JUDGE DREDD**

IN ORBIT EVERY MONDAY

30p
EARTH
MONEY
Prog 572

30 APR 1988

$1.80 Malaysia
95c Australia
$1.00 New Zealand (Inc. G.S.T.)
25g Mercury
500g Venus
75g Mars
965g Pluto
-2g Neptune

HITMAN
PART THREE

JUDGE DREDD

DR FRANK GILBRET, AGE 41, RESIDENT BISHOP MOUNSEY. HAD AN OFFICE HERE FOR THE LAST FOUR YEARS.

PROBABLE CAUSE OF DEATH, CYANIDE POISONING.

COUGHLIN, PICK UP A SEARCH SQUAD AND CHECK HIS HOME. WIFE MIGHT KNOW SOMETHING. YOU CAN HAVE THE PLEASURE OF INFORMING HER.

THANKS.

GILBRET HAVE FAMILY?

WIFE IN MOUNSEY.

'KAY, LET US KNOW IF YOU COME UP WITH ANYTHING ELSE.

SCRIPT
WAGNER/GRANT
ART
J. BAIKIE
LETTERING
J. POTTER

SIMMONS, GET BUSY ON E TO J. TRY TAX AND BANK RECORDS — THE USUAL STUFF. REQUEST PERSONNEL FROM CENTRAL.

WILCO

CYANIDE POISONING?

YES, DEAD BEFORE THE FIRE.

SELF-ADMINISTERED?

UNLIKELY.

SOMEONE EMPTIED ONE OF THE CABINETS— FILES *E* TO *J*, RELATED RECORDS, APPOINTMENT BOOKS, ETCETERA... MADE A PRETTY GOOD JOB OF BURNING THEM.

HMM... THAT SUGGESTS A PATIENT TRYING TO COVER THEIR TRACKS.

KEEP ME INFORMED.

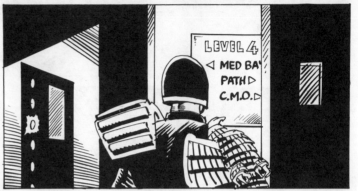

ALMOST THERE... KEEP GOING!

CAN YOU BELIEVE THIS, DOC? RIGHT UNDER THEIR NOSES!

DREDD J CAT

THIS IS GOING TO BE THE BEST ...THE BEST EVER!

WAKE UP!

DREDD - J

CONTROL, WE GOT A JUDGE *BULLET* CURRENTLY ON THE ROSTER?

NEGATIVE.

BULLET— ISN'T THAT THE JUDGES' NAME IN THAT PLAY... "A BULLET FOR THE MAN"?

YEAH. WE GOT CONFIRMATION ON THAT. HE GOES DOWN FIGHTING IN ACT THREE.

HELL!

WARN MED BAY! HE'S AFTER DREDD!

OVER RIDE

I HIRED THE UNIFORM FROM A THEATRICAL COSTUMIERS. THEY MADE ME SIGN A PLEDGE NOT TO USE IT FOR ADVERTISING. NOT LIKE I'M GOING TO ADVERTISE, IS IT?

CARE TO TELL ME WHY, CREEP?

OH, THE CHALLENGE... THE WARM FEELING OF SATISFACTION I'M GOING TO GET KNOWING THAT *I'M* THE ONE WHO FINALLY PUT YOU AWAY.

PROG 547
7 NOV 87

2000AD
FEATURING JUDGE DREDD

$1.70 Malaysia
75c Australia
85c New Zealand
(Inc. G.S.T.)
88g Mercury
210g Venus
66g Mars
110g Saturn
2g Pluto
429g Neptune

28p EARTH MONEY

IN ORBIT EVERY MONDAY

CHOPPER

OUT!

CLIFF ROBINSON -87-